THE SON
PAUL SIMON PIANO

Order No. PS 11097
US International Standard Book Number: 0.8256.3306.0
UK International Standard Book Number: 0.7119.1661.6

Exclusive Distributors:
Music Sales Corporation
257 Park Avenue South, New York, NY 10010 USA
Music Sales Limited
8/9 Frith Street, London W1V 5TZ England
Music Sales Pty. Limited
120 Rothschild Street, Rosebery, Sydney, NSW 2018, Australia

Printed in the United States of America by
Vicks Lithograph and Printing Corporation

Amsco Publications
New York/London/Sydney

Slip Slidin' Away

Words and Music by PAUL SIMON

tell him all the rea-sons for the things he'd done. He came a

long way _____ just to ex - plain. _____

He kissed his boy as he lay sleep-ing, then he turned a-round and head-ed home a -

gain. Slip slid - in' a - way,

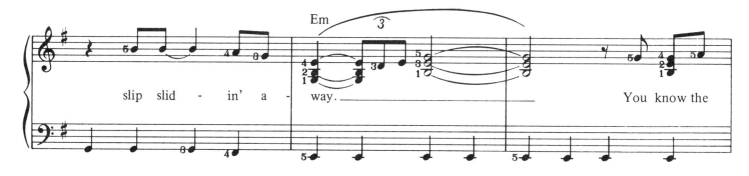

slip slid - in' a - way. _____ You know the

near-er your des-ti - na - tion the more___ you're slip slid - in' a - way.___

D.%. al Coda

⊕CODA

God on - ly knows___

Slip slid - in' a -

way, ___

slip slid - in' a - way.___

You know the

near - er your des - ti - na - tion the more___

___you're slip slid - in' a - way. ___

Repeat to Fade

Slip slid - in' a -

7

American Tune

Words and Music by PAUL SIMON

dy - ing,

I dreamed that my soul___ rose un - ex -

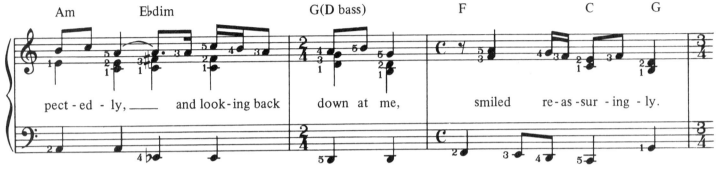

pect - ed - ly,___ and look - ing back

down at me,

smiled re - as - sur - ing - ly.

And I dreamed I was

fly - ing,

and high up a - bove___

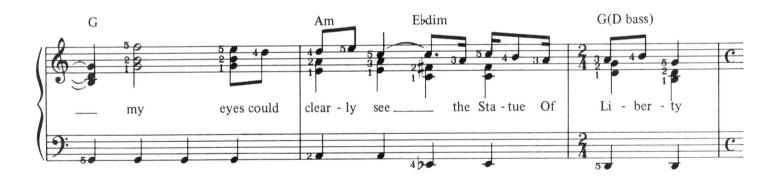

___ my

eyes could

clear - ly see___ the Sta - tue Of

Li - ber - ty

sail - ing a - way to sea,___

and I dreamed I was

fly - ing.

Still, to-mor-rows goin' to be an-oth-er work - ing

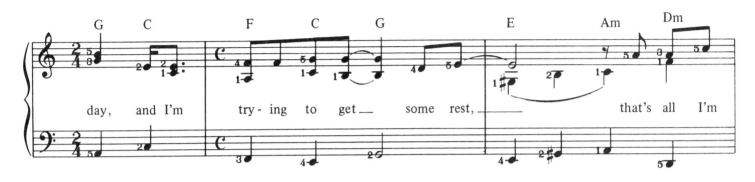

day, and I'm try-ing to get some rest, that's all I'm

try - ing to get some rest.

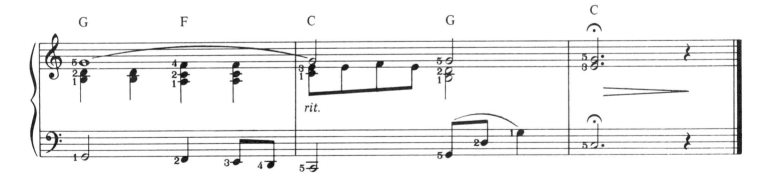

rit.

2. I don't know a soul who's not been battered, I don't have a friend who feels at ease.
I don't know a dream that's not been shattered or driven to its knees.
Oh, but it's alright, it's alright, for we lived so well so long,
Still, when I think of the road we're trav'ling on, I wonder what's gone wrong,
I can't help it, I wonder what's gone wrong. *etc.*

Have A Good Time

Words and Music by PAUL SIMON

Moderately, with a blues feeling

Yes - ter - day it was my birth - day; I
2. 3. (See block lyric)

hung one more year on the line. _____ I should be de - pressed; my life's

_____ a mess, but I'm hav-ing a good time. _____ Oo, _____ I've been

lov - ing and lov - ing and lov - ing; I'm ex -

haust - ed from lov - ing so well. _____ I should go to bed,_ but a

voice in my head says, *(Spoken)* "Aw, what the hell!" Have a good time,

have a good time, _____

have a good time, _____ have a good time.

(2.) Par - a (3.) May - be I'm _____

2. Paranoia strikes deep in the heartland, but I think it's all overdone.
   Exaggerating this, exaggerating that; they don't have no fun.
   I don't believe what I read in the papers; they're just out to capture my dime.
   I ain't worrying and I ain't scurrying; I'm having a good time.
   Have a good time, *etc.* - - - - -

3. Maybe I'm laughing my way to disaster, maybe my race has been run.
   Maybe I'm blind to the fate of mankind, but what can be done?
   So God bless the goods we was given, and God bless the U.S. of A.
   And God bless our standard of living; let's keep it that way, and we'll
   all have a good time, *etc.* - - - - -

15

Bridge Over Troubled Water

Words and Music by PAUL SIMON

All your dreams are on their way.   See how they

F   C   F   C   F   C   G   Am

shine.   Oh,   if you need a friend,   I'm sail-ing

G   G7   C   C7

right be - hind, ___ Like a bridge o - ver troub-led wa-ter,

F   G   C7   F   C dim   C   Am

I will ease your mind,   Like a bridge o - ver troub - led wa-ter,

F   Am   E7   Am   C7   F   D   C   Am

I will ease your mind. ___

F   E7   Am   D7   G   C   F   C

Me And Julio Down By The Schoolyard

Words and Music by PAUL SIMON

saw, it was a-gainst the law. The

ma-ma looked down__ and__ spit on the ground ev-'ry time my__ name gets
coup-le of days they came and take me a-way, but the press let the sto-ry

men - tioned.__ The pa-pa said "Oy, if I get that boy__ I'm gon-na
leak. __ And when the rad-ic-al priest come to get me re-leased__ we's

stick him in the house of de-ten-tion."} Well, I'm on my
all__ on the cov-er of News-week. }

way, __ I don't know where I'm go-ing,__ I'm on my

20

Cecilia

Words and Music by PAUL SIMON

Cel - ia, you're break-ing my heart,___ you're shak-ing my con - fid -ence dai - ly.___ Oh, Ce-

cil - ia, I'm down on my knees,___ I'm beg - ging you please_ to come home.___

___ Ho - ho - home. ___

Mak-ing love ___ in the af - ter-noon_ with Ce -

cil - ia, up in my __ bed - room, __ I got up __ to wash my face, __ when I

F   C7   F   B♭

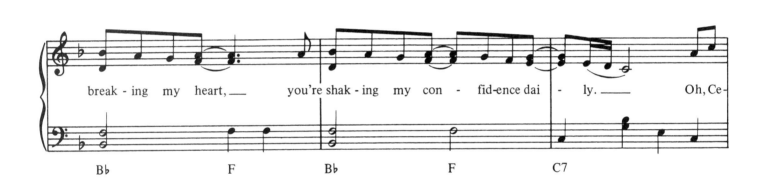

come back to bed __ some - one's tak - en my place. __ Cel - ia, you're

F   C7   F

break - ing my heart, __ you're shak - ing my con - fid-ence dai - ly. __ Oh, Ce-

B♭   F   B♭   F   C7

cil - ia, I'm down on my knees, __ I'm beg - ging you please __ to come home

B♭   F   B♭   F   B♭   F

__ Come on home.   Poh poh poh poh __ poh poh poh

C   F

23

poh poh poh poh poh poh. Ju-bi-la - tion, she loves me a-gain, I

Bb   C7   Bb   F   Bb   F

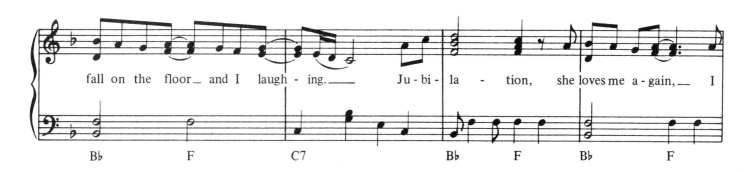

fall on the floor and I laugh-ing. Ju-bi-la - tion, she loves me a-gain, I

Bb   F   C7   Bb   F   Bb   F

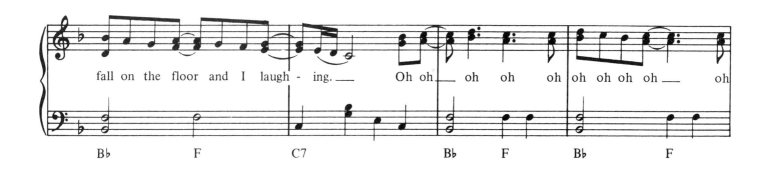

fall on the floor and I laugh-ing. Oh oh oh oh oh oh oh oh oh oh

Bb   F   C7   Bb   F   Bb   F

oh oh oh oh oh oh oh oh. Oh oh oh oh oh oh oh oh oh oh

Bb   F   C7   Bb   F   Bb   F

rall. . . . .

oh oh oh oh oh oh oh oh. Come on home.

Bb   F   C7   F

24

Take Me To The Mardi Gras

Words and Music by PAUL SIMON

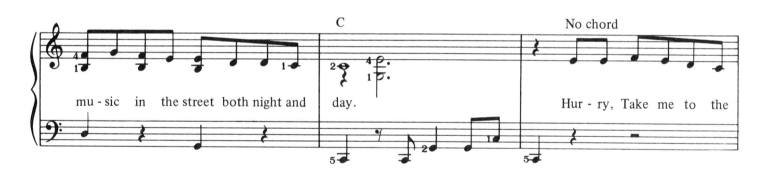

you can le - gal -ize your laws, you can wear your sum-mer clothes__ in the New Or -

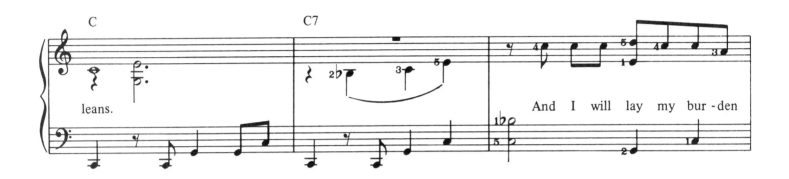

leans. And I will lay my bur -den

down,_____ rest my head up - on that shore,

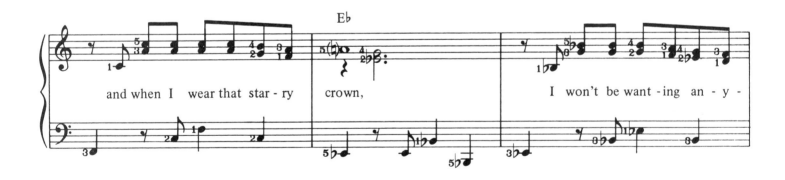

and when I wear that star - ry crown, I won't be want -ing an - y -

more.____ Take your bur-dens to the

The Boxer

Words and Music by PAUL SIMON

left my home and my fam - i - ly, ___ I was no more than a boy, in the

com - pa - ny ___ of stran - gers, in the qui - et of a rail - way sta - tion

run - ning scared. ___ Lay - ing low, seek - ing

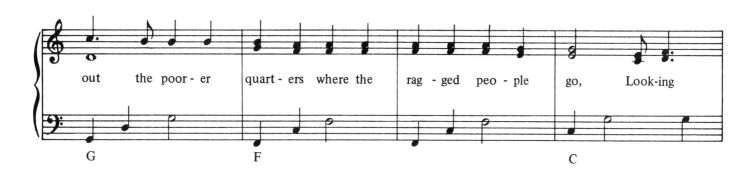

out the poor - er quart - ers where the rag - ged peo - ple go, Look - ing

for the pla - ces on - ly they would know. Lie - la

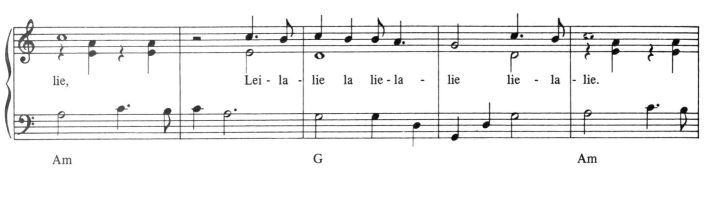

lie, Lei - la - lie la lie - la - lie lie - la - lie.

Am   G   Am

Lie - la - lie la la la la lie,____ la la la la lie. _____ Ask-ing

F   C   F   C   F6   C   F6

on - ly work-man's wag - es, I come look-ing for a job, but I get no of - fers. ____

C   Am   G

____ Just a come-on from the whores on Sev-enth Av - e - nue. _____

Dm   C

I do de - clare, there were times ____ when I was so lone-some, I

Am   G   F

took some comfort there. Ooo-la - la - la-la - la-la - la. _____ Then I'm

C   G

lay - ing out my winter clothes and wish-ing I was gone, _____ go-ing

C   Am

home, _____ Where the New York Ci-ty win - ters are - n't

G   Dm   G7   C

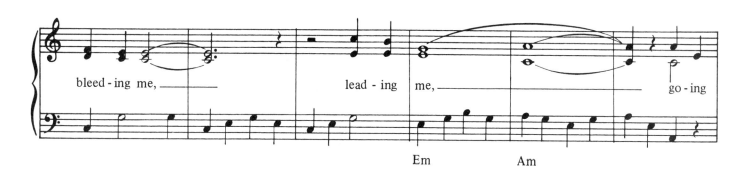

bleed - ing me, _____ lead - ing me, _____ go-ing

Em   Am

home. _____ In the clear-ing stands a box-er, and a fight-er by his

G   C

Graceland

Words and Music by PAUL SIMON

The Mis - sis - sip - pi Del - ta was shin - ing like a na - tion - al gui -

tar.   I am fol - low - ing the riv - er down the

high - way through the cra - dle of the Ci - vil war.

I'm go - ing to Grace - land, Grace - land in
(2. 3.) *(See block lyric)*

To Coda ✆

But I've rea - son to be - lieve we both ___

___ will be re - ceived in Grace - land.

She comes back to tell me she's gone. ___

As if I did - n't know that, as

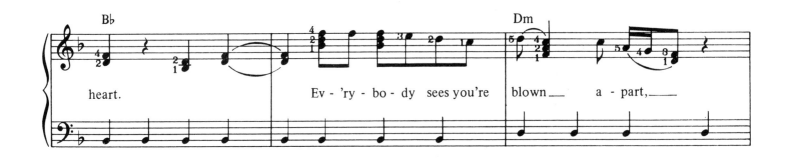

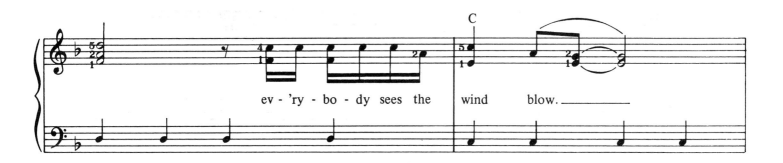

ev - 'ry - bo - dy sees the wind blow. _____

1. I'm go - ing to Grace-

2. I'm go - ing to Grace-

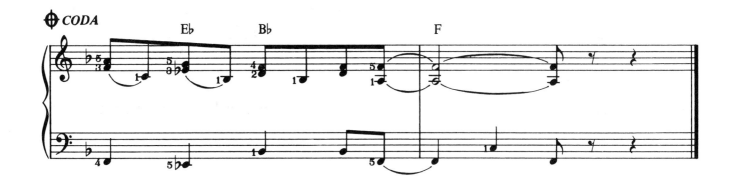

2. I'm going to Graceland, Memphis, Tennessee. I'm going to Graceland.
   Poor boys and pilgrims with families and we are going to Graceland.
   My trav'lling companions are ghosts and empty sockets.
   I'm lookin' at ghosts and empties.
   But I've reason to believe we all will be received in Graceland.
   There is a girl in New York City who calls herself the human trampoline,
   and sometimes when I'm falling, flying or tumbling in turmoil I say,
   oh, so this is what she means. She means we're bouncing into Graceland.
   And I see losing love is like a window in your heart.
   Ev'rybody sees you're blown apart, ev'rybody feels the wind blow.

3. I'm going to Graceland. I'm going to Graceland.
   For reasons I cannot explain, there's some part of me wants to see Graceland.
   And I may be obliged to defend ev'ry love, ev'ry ending
   or maybe there's no obligations, now.
   Maybe I've reason to believe we all will be received in Graceland.

The Boy In The Bubble

Music by PAUL SIMON and FORERE MOTLOHELOA
Words by PAUL SIMON

(1.) It was a slow day and the sun was beat - ing on the
(2.) dry wind and it swept a - cross the des - ert and
(3.) *(See block lyric)*

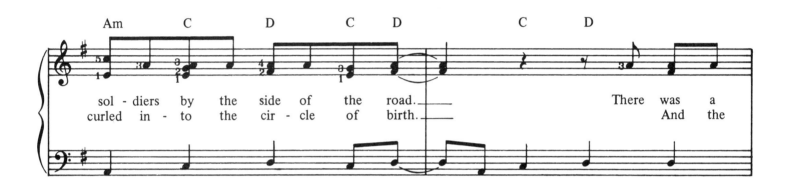

sol - diers by the side of the road. There was a
curled in - to the cir - cle of birth. And the

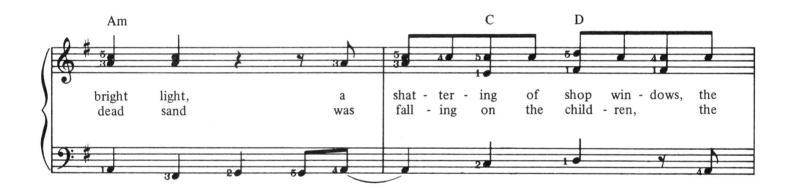

bright light, a shat - ter - ing of shop win - dows, the
dead sand was fall - ing on the child - ren, the

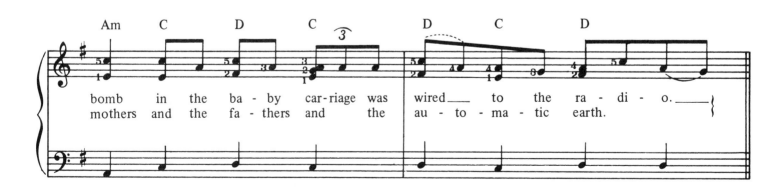

bomb in the ba - by car - riage was wired to the ra - di - o.
mothers and the fa - thers and was the au - to - ma - tic earth.

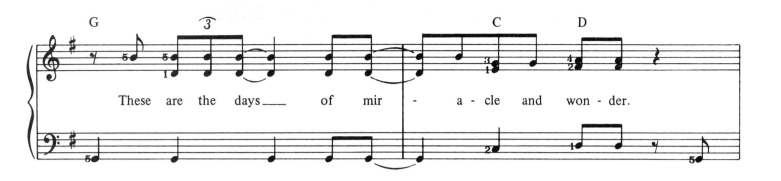

These are the days___ of mir - a - cle and won - der.

This is the long___ dis - tance call.

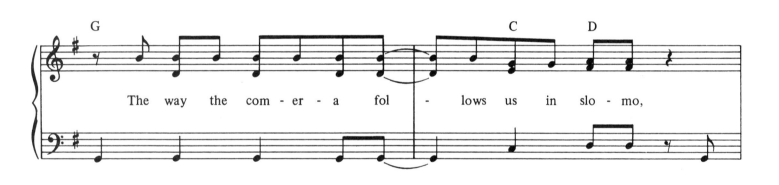

The way the com - er - a fol - lows us in slo - mo,

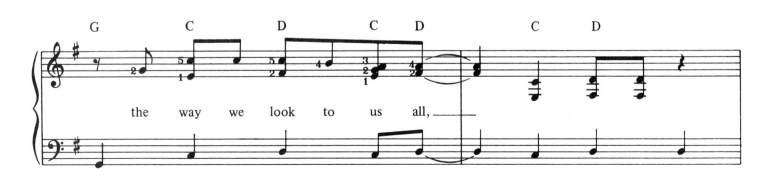

the way we look to us all,___

the way we look to a dis - tant con - stel - la - tion that's

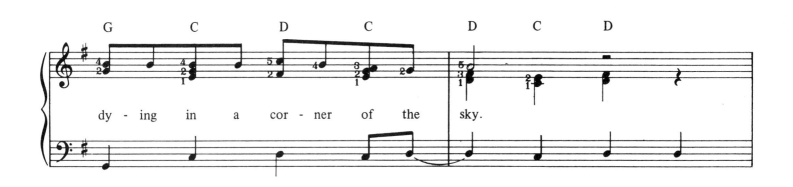

dy - ing in a cor - ner of the sky.

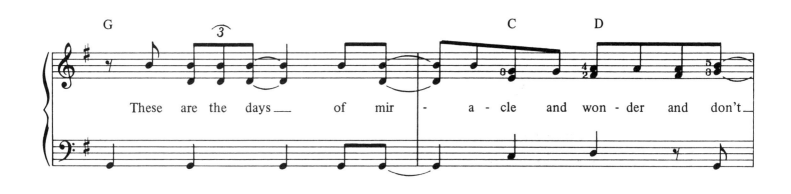

These are the days ___ of mir - a - cle and won - der and don't ___

___ cry, ba - by, don't cry, ___ don't cry. ___

3. It's a turn around jump-shot,
   it's ev'rybody jump start, it's ev'ry generation throws a hero up the pop-charts.
   Medicine is magical and magical is art.
   There go the boy in the bubble and the baby with the baboon heart.
   These are the days of lasers in the jungle,
   lasers in the jungle somewhere.
   Staccato signals of constant information,
   a loose affiliation of millionaires and billionaires and baby:
   These are the days of miracle and wonder.
   This is the long distance call.
   The way the camera follows us in slomo,
   the way we look to us all, don't cry, don't cry.

Mrs. Robinson

Words and Music by PAUL SIMON

VERSE

like to know a lit - tle bit a - bout___ you for our files._

A7   D   A   Em7 A7

We'd like to help___ you learn to help your-

D   A7   D

self._____

Look a - round you, all you see___ are

D9   G   Dm   C

sym - path - et - ic eyes._____

F   Dm   A

D. S. al Coda

___ the grounds___ un - til you feel at home.___ And here's to

G   A   G

43

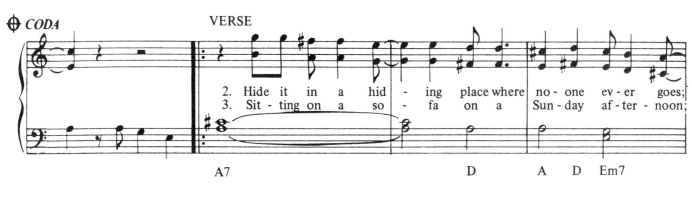

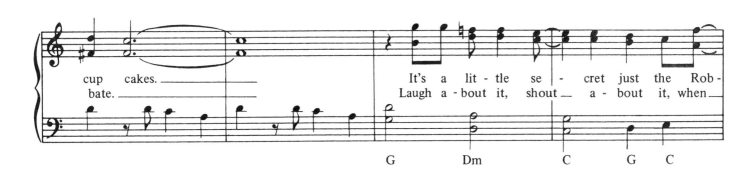

CHORUS

45

Mother And Child Reunion

Words and Music by PAUL SIMON

oh _____ lit - tle dar - ling of mine._____

(1.) I can't for the life of me _____ re - mem-ber a
(2.) *(See block lyric)*

sad - der day, I know they say let it be,_____

But it just won't work out that way,

And the course of a life - time runs

2. I just can't believe it's so, and though it seems strange to say,
   I never been laid so low — in such a mysterious way,
   And the course of a lifetime runs over and over again.
   But I would not give you false hope, *etc.*

49

Diamonds On The Soles Of Her Shoes

Words and Music by PAUL SIMON

She's a rich girl, she don't try to hide it; dia-

-monds on the soles of her shoes. He's a poor

boy, emp-ty as a pock-et, emp-ty as a pock-et with noth-

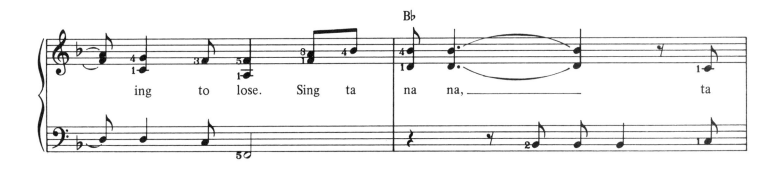

-ing to lose. Sing ta na na, ta

52

ev -'ry - bo - dy here would know ex - act - ly what I was talk - ing a - bout.___ Talk- in' 'bout

dia-monds on the soles___ of her shoes. ___

2. She makes the sign of the teaspoon, he makes the sign of the wave.
   The poor boy changes clothes and he puts on aftershave to compensate for his ordinary shoes.
   And she said "Honey, take me dancing," but they ended up by sleeping in a doorway
   by the bodegas and the lights on upper Broadway, wearing diamonds on the soles of their shoes.
   And I could say oo - - - - - - - - And ev'rybody knows what I'm talking about.
   I mean ev'rybody here would know exactly what I was talking about.
   Talkin' 'bout diamonds on the soles of her shoes.

El Condor Pasa
(If I Could)

English Lyric by PAUL SIMON

Musical arrangement by JORGE MILCHBERG and DANIEL ROBLES

Fairly slowly

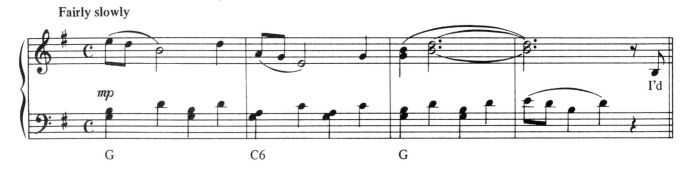

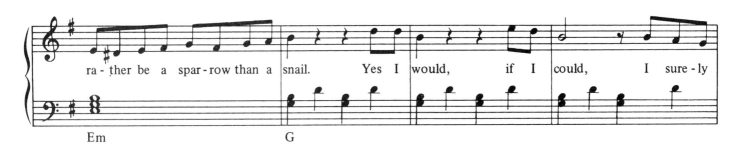

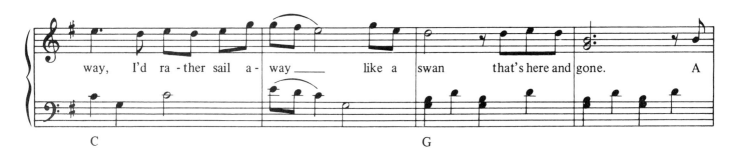

Fifty Ways To Leave Your Lover

Words and Music by PAUL SIMON

59

The 59th Street Bridge Song
(Feelin' Groovy)
Words and Music by PAUL SIMON

Moderato

Repeat and fade

61

The Sound Of Silence

Words and Music by PAUL SIMON

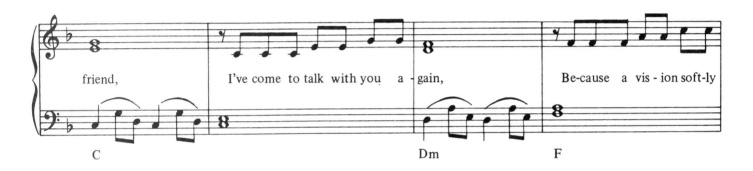

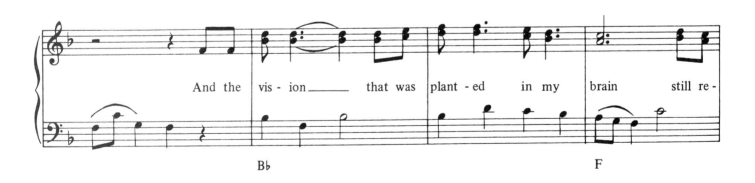

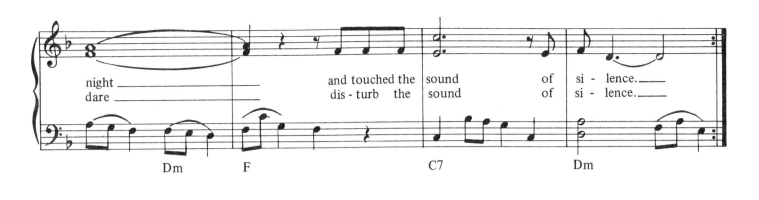

night _____ _____ and touched the sound of si - lence. _____
dare _____ _____ dis-turb the sound of si - lence. _____

Dm   F   C7   Dm

4. "Fools!" said I, "you do not know, si - lence like a can-cer grows."

C   Dm

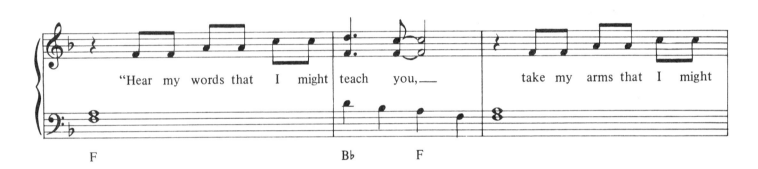

"Hear my words that I might teach you, — take my arms that I might

F   B♭   F

reach you." — But my words like si - lent rain-drops

B♭   F   B♭

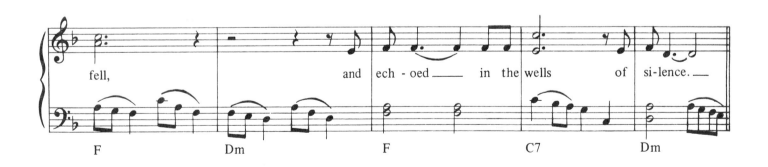

fell, and ech - oed _____ in the wells of si - lence. _____

F   Dm   F   C7   Dm

5. And the peo-ple bowed and prayed to the ne-on god they made, and the sign flashed out its warn - ing,___ in the words that it was form-ing.___ And the sign said "The words of the pro-phets are writ-ten on the sub-way walls _____ and ten-e-ment halls," and whis-pered _____ in the sounds of si-lence.

You Can Call Me Al

Words and Music by PAUL SIMON

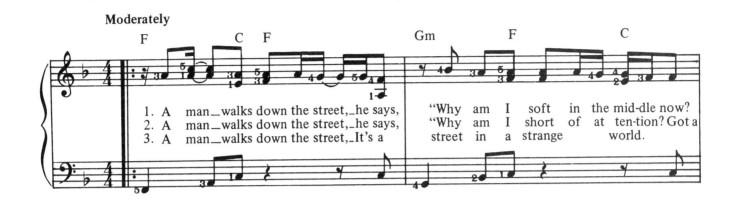

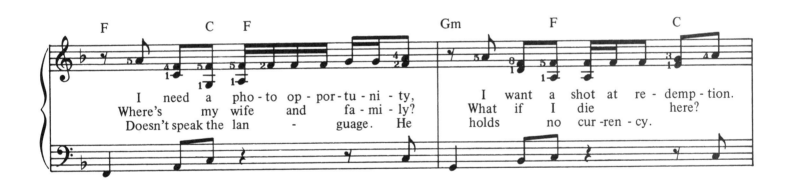

66

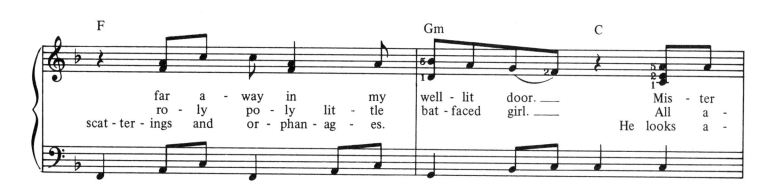

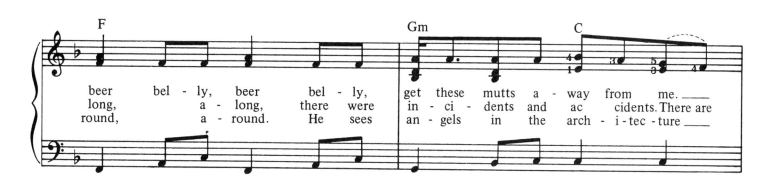

67

To Coda ⊕

If you'll be my bo-dy-guard __ I can be your long __ lost __ pal. ____ I can call you Bet - ty and Bet - ty, when you call me, you can

1. call me Al. ____

2. call me Al. ____ Call me Al. ____

Loves Me Like A Rock

Words and Music by PAUL SIMON

(1.) When I was a lit - tle boy,

and the de - vil would call my name,

I'd say "Now who do,_____

who do you think you're fool - ing?"

I'm a con - se - cra - ted boy.

I'm a sing - er in the Sun - day choir,_____

oh,_____ my ma - ma loves me, she loves_____

_____ me. She get down on her knees and hug_____ me like She

Loves Me Like A Rock. She rocks me like the

rock of a - ges and loves ____ me. ____

She love me, love me, love me, love me. ____

No chord

(2.) When I was grown to be a man,

and the de - vil would call my name.

I'd say, "Now who do, ___ who do you think you're fool -

ing?"   I'm a con - su - ma - ted man,

I can snatch a lit - tle pu - ri - ty, ___ my ma - ma loves

___ me,   she loves ___ me.   she get down on her knees and hug ___

___ me like She   Love   Me Like A   Rock.

She rocks me like the   rock of a - ges and loves ___ me.

She love me, love me, love me, love me.___ (3.) And if I was the Pre - si -

dent, the min-ute the Con-gress call my name.

I say "Now who do,___ who do you think you're fool -

ing?" I've got the Pre - si - den - tial Seal,

I'm up on the Pres - i - den - tial Po - di - um.___

My ma - ma loves _ me, she loves _ me. She

get down on her knees and hug _ me like She Loves Me Like A

Rock. She rocks me like the rock of a - ges and loves _

_ me. _ She love me, love me, love me, love me. _

Repeat to Fade

She love me, love me, love me, love me. _

My Little Town

Words and Music by PAUL SIMON

school; rid-ing my bike past the gates of the fac-tor-ies;

Em   Gm   C7   F

My mom—do-ing the laun—dry,— hang-ing our

D7   Eb7   Ab   Eb   Eb+

shirts in the dir—ty breeze. And af—ter it

G7   C

rains———— there's a rain—bow, and all of the col—ours are

F   G7

black. It's not that the col—ours aren't there; it's just im-ag-i-

C   Dm   C

Scarborough Fair

Arrangement and original counter melody by PAUL SIMON and ARTHUR GARFUNKEL

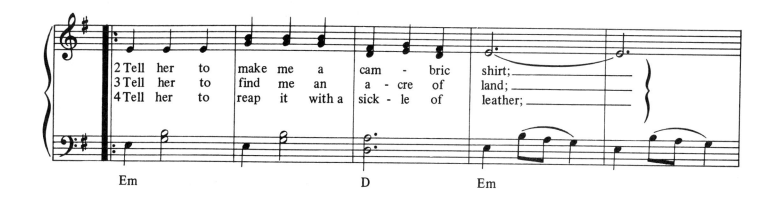

2 Tell her to make me a cam - bric shirt; _____
3 Tell her to find me an a - cre of land; _____
4 Tell her to reap it with a sick - le of leather; _____

Em   D   Em

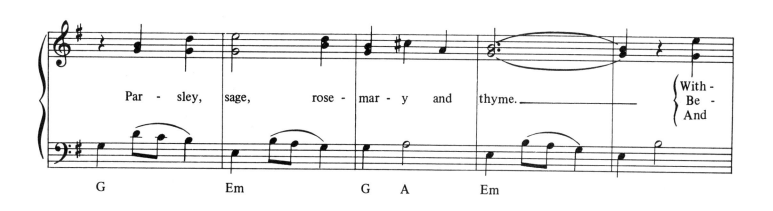

Par - sley, sage, rose - mar - y and thyme. _____

With -
Be -
And

G   Em   G   A   Em

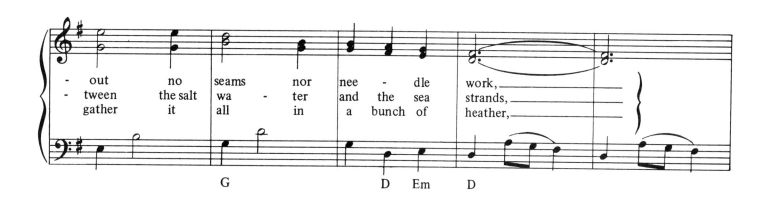

- out no seams nor nee - dle work, _____
- tween the salt wa - ter and the sea strands, _____
gather it all in a bunch of heather, _____

G   D Em   D

D.S. al fine

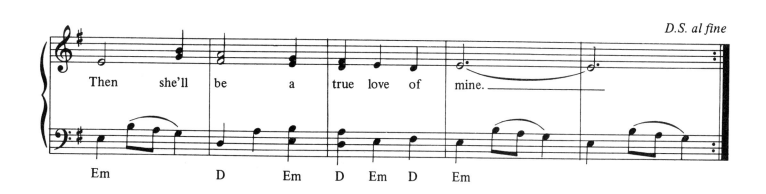

Then she'll be a true love of mine. _____

Em   D   Em D Em D Em

I Am A Rock

Words and Music by PAUL SIMON

Fairly slowly

mp

C

1. A win - ter's

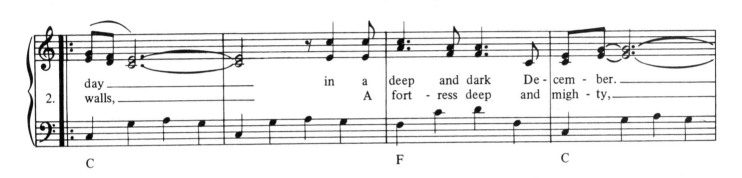

day _____ in a deep and dark De - cem - ber. _____

2. walls, _____ A fort - ress deep and migh - ty, _____

C   F   C

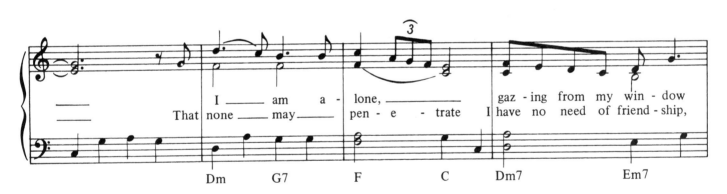

_____ I _____ am a - lone, _____ gaz - ing from my win - dow

That none _____ may _____ pen - e - trate I have no need of friend - ship,

Dm   G7   F   C   Dm7   Em7

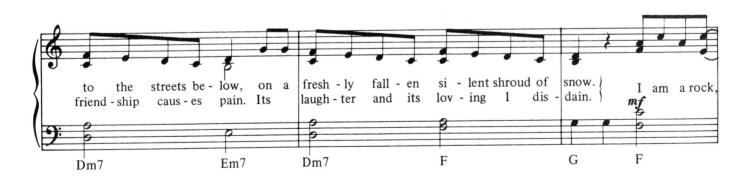

to the streets be - low, on a fresh - ly fall - en si - lent shroud of snow. ⎱

friend - ship caus - es pain. Its laugh - ter and its lov - ing I dis - dain. ⎰

mf

Dm7   Em7   Dm7   F   G   F

I am a rock,

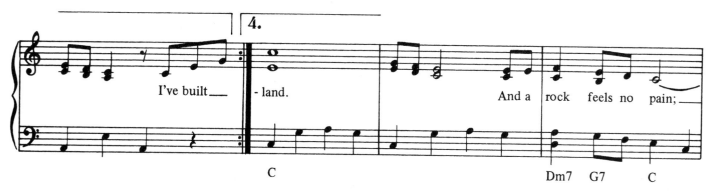

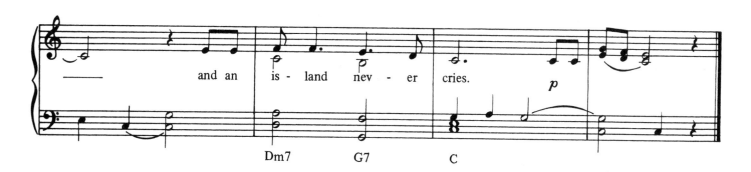

3. Don't talk of love, but I've heard the word before;
   It's sleeping in my memory.
   I won't disturb the slumber of feelings that have died.
   If I never loved I never would have cried.
   I am a rock, I am an island.

4. I have my books and my poetry to protect me,
   I am shielded in my armour.
   Hiding in my room, safe within my womb,
   I touch no one and no one touches me.
   I am a rock, I am an island.

Homeward Bound

Words and Music by PAUL SIMON

Moderato

C   F6   G7

I'm

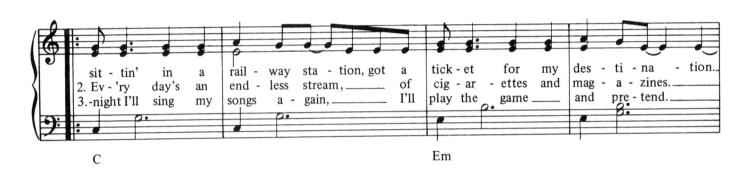

1. sit - tin' in a rail - way sta - tion, got a tick - et for my des - ti - na - tion.
2. Ev - 'ry day's an end - less stream, ___ of cig - ar - ettes and mag - a - zines.
3. -night I'll sing my songs a - gain, ___ I'll play the game ___ and pre - tend.

C   Em

Mm ___   On a tour ___ of
Mm ___   And each town looks ___ the
Mm ___   But all my words ___ come

Gm   C   A   Dm

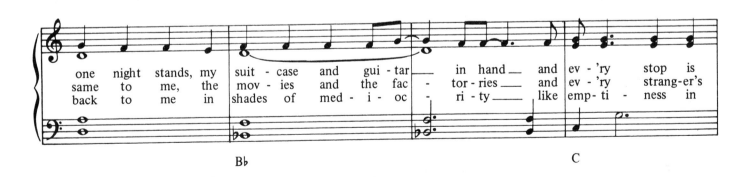

one night stands, my suit - case and gui - tar ___ in hand ___ and ev - 'ry stop is
same to me, the mov - ies and the fac - tor - ries ___ and ev - 'ry strang - er's
back to me in shades of med - i - oc - ri - ty ___ like emp - ti - ness in

Bb   C

neat - ly planned_ for a po - et and a one - man band._
face I see___ re - minds me that I long_ to be._
har - mo - ny___ I need some - one to com - fort me.

CHORUS

Home - ward_ bound, I wish I was,___ Home - ward_ bound._

C   F   C   F

___ Home, where my thought's_ es - cap-ing, Home, where my mu - sic's play-ing,

C   Dm C Bb F   C   Dm C Bb F

Home, where my love___ lies wait - ing, si - lent - ly for me.___

C   Dm C Bb F G7   C

2. —
3. To

3.
rall.

si - lent - ly for me.

C   Cmaj7   G   C7   C   F6   C

Still Crazy After All These Years

Words and Music by PAUL SIMON